Discover
LIFE
LONG AGO

Reading
CHALLENGE®

Illustrations Copyright © 2004 Orpheus Books Ltd
2 Church Green, Witney, Oxon OX28 4AW

Illustrated by Peter Dennis (Linda Rogers Associates)

Text and Design Copyright © 2005 Reading Challenge, Inc.
www.readingchallenge.com

0705-1W

Visit us at www.readingchallenge.com

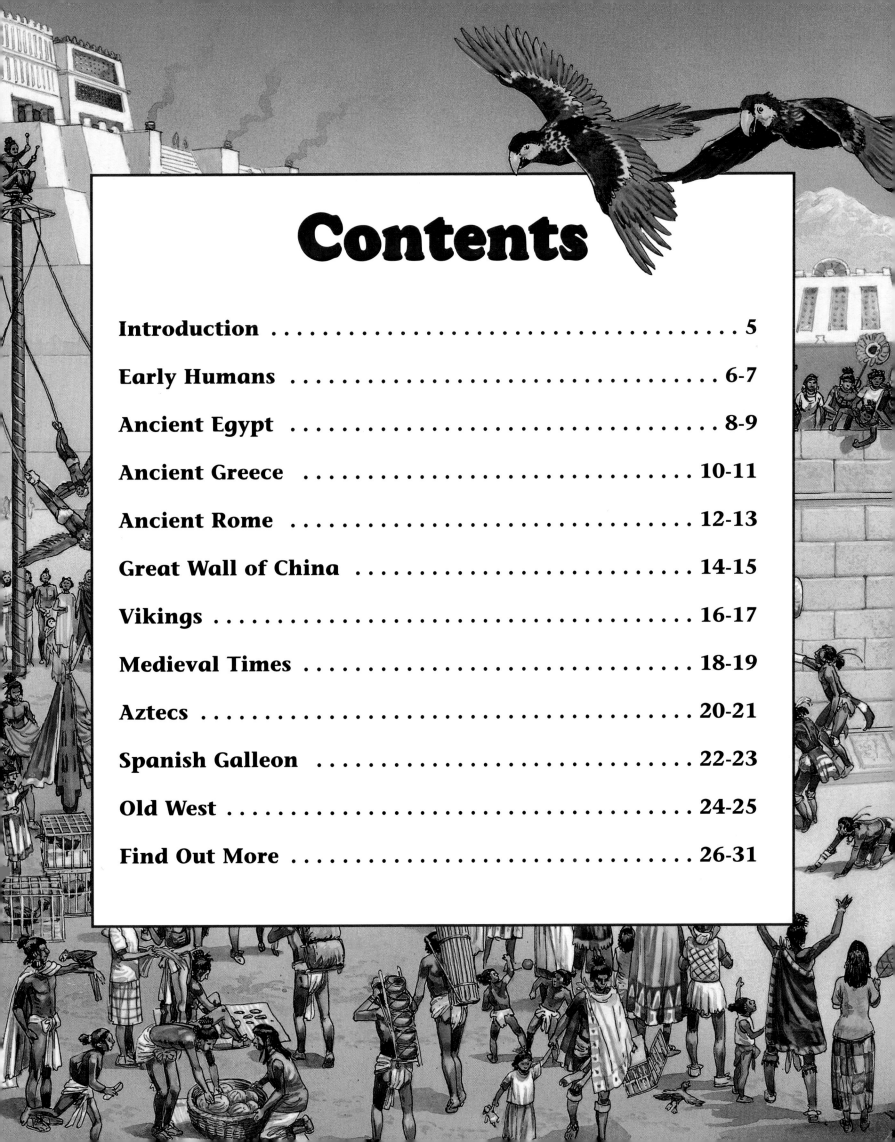

Contents

Introduction

Imagine living in ancient Rome or traveling on the high seas with pirates. What would it be like to live in those times? What would you wear? What would you eat?

LIFE LONG AGO takes you on an incredible adventure. Each panoramic illustration gives you a glimpse into the world of yesterday. Fun search and find activities will help you identify the people, places, and interesting things that were important throughout history.

More fun awaits in the **Find Out More** section in the back of the book, which is packed with tidbits, trivia, and websites to learn more about each subject.

So put on your thinking cap and get ready to
Read, Search & Find™ as you
Discover
LIFE LONG AGO!

Early Humans

Life for early humans was very different from life today. People had to hunt animals and collect nuts and berries for food. Animal skins and furs were used for making clothes and tents. Tools and spears were made from sticks and stones. It was hard for early humans to survive.

Search & Find

- [ ] Birds (4)
- [ ] Mammoths (8)
- [ ] Mouse
- [ ] Spears (16)
- [ ] Tool makers (2)
- [ ] Torches (3)
- [ ] Wolf
- [ ] Woman carrying a baby

Fire
Early humans learned how to make and use fire. It was a great discovery!

Fishing
Boys learned how to hunt and fish with spears by watching the older men.

Tent
People often slept on the ground in a tent or a cave.

Mammoth
A mammoth was a kind of elephant.

Hunting
Hunting giant mammoths took a lot of people!

Clothing
Animal skins and fur were used for clothes and to cover feet.

Gathering berries
Women and children collected plants, nuts, and berries.

Spears
A sharpened stone was tied onto the end of a wooden pole to make a spear.

Find Out More
on page 26

7

Ancient Egypt

A long time ago, Egypt was ruled by powerful kings. They were called pharaohs (FARE-ohz). When a pharaoh died, he was buried in a pyramid (PIR-uh-mid). It took thousands of workers to build a pyramid. The workers used special tools to carve huge blocks of stone. It could take between 20 and 40 years to complete a pyramid.

Search & Find

- [ ] Boats (3)
- [ ] Dogs (2)
- [ ] Fire
- [ ] Guard
- [ ] Mules (4)
- [ ] Runaway sled
- [ ] Water jugs (19)
- [ ] Woman holding flower

Boat

Egyptians traveled the Nile River by boat. The boats carried many things to be traded with people in other cities.

Workers

Workers dragged each heavy stone block up the side of the pyramid.

Pyramid

The largest pyramid, in Giza (Gee-zah), Egypt, contains more than two million blocks of stone!

Tools

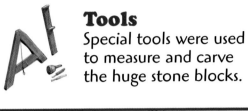

Special tools were used to measure and carve the huge stone blocks.

Pharaoh

The people believed that the pharaoh was like a god. The pharoah owned Egypt and everything in it.

High priest

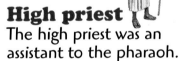

The high priest was an assistant to the pharaoh.

Pack mule

Mules and donkeys were used to carry supplies to the work site.

Find Out More on page 27

Ancient Greece

Ancient Greece is famous for many things. The ancient Greeks lived in small areas called city-states. In some of them, the government was ruled by the people. That had never happened before. People wrote poetry and performed plays. The Greeks built great temples and statues. They honored their gods and heroes.

Search & Find

- ☐ **Boys stealing grapes**
- ☐ **Dogs (2)**
- ☐ **Donkeys (6)**
- ☐ **"Flying" actor**
- ☐ **Leaking water jug**
- ☐ **Man falling down stairs**
- ☐ **Man trying on sandals**
- ☐ **Soldiers with spears (18)**

Actor
All the actors in ancient Greek plays were men.

Sculptor
A sculptor is an artist who creates statues.

Public speaker
A citizen could share his ideas with other people in the square.

Doctor
Greek doctors made many new discoveries. Their healing methods were used for hundreds of years.

Army
Each city-state had its own army.

Weaver
A weaver makes cloth. The Greeks were famous for weaving a cloth called linen.

Ox cart
Oxen pulled carts that carried goods and crops into the cities.

Temple
The ancient Greeks worshiped inside temples.

Find Out More
on page 27

Ancient Rome

Search & Find

- [ ] **Blue shields (3)**
- [ ] **Dogs (2)**
- [ ] **Doves (2)**
- [ ] **Fountain**
- [ ] **Ladder**
- [ ] **Mouse**
- [ ] **Men blowing trumpets (2)**
- [ ] **Stubborn donkey**

Ancient Rome was the center of the Roman Empire. The Empire included much of Europe, the Middle East, and the northern coast of Africa. Stone roads connected all the areas to Rome. In the city of Rome, there were busy markets and many temples. Rome also had running water, sewers, and public baths.

Statue
Statues of emperors and religious figures were put in public places.

Stepping stones
Large stones were placed in the street for people to walk across.

Public baths
The Romans loved to visit the public baths. There they could sit in steam rooms and swim in warm pools.

Emporer

Caesar (SEE-zur) Augustus was the first emperor of the Roman Empire. He renamed the month of August after himself.

Bakery

Rome had many of the same shops that we have today. There were food sellers, shoe stores, and bakeries.

Gladiators

Gladiators entertained people. They fought with each other in an arena. Sometimes they fought wild animals.

Soldiers

A Roman soldier carried a spear, a shield, and a short sword. Each soldier was part of a legion (LEE-jun). A legion was a large group of about 5,000 men.

Find Out More
on page 28

Great Wall of China

The Great Wall was built by Chinese emperors. They wanted to keep enemies out of northern China. Workers built watch towers and forts along the wall. Soldiers walked back and forth along the top, watching for invaders. The wall passes over mountains and deserts. It is one of the greatest structures ever built.

Search & Find

- ☐ Crossbows (2)
- ☐ Falling rocks
- ☐ Flags (4)
- ☐ Horses (10)
- ☐ Ladders (5)
- ☐ Umbrella
- ☐ Wheel carts (2)
- ☐ Whips (2)

Watchtower
Towers were placed all along the wall for guards to watch for enemy invaders.

Bricklayers
Thousands of workers were needed to build the Great Wall.

Rock quarry
A quarry is a place where stone is dug out of the ground. The stone is cut into smaller pieces and used to build many things.

Carving
A worker chips away at a large stone to shape it into a smaller one.

Soldiers
Soldiers would send up smoke signals or fire a cannon if trouble was coming.

Emperor
The emperor protected his land and his people.

Find Out More on page 28

Vikings

The Vikings came from the area that is now known as Denmark, Sweden, and Norway. They traveled by sea and traded with people in faraway lands. Vikings also raided many villages they came upon. They often settled in the villages they raided. Vikings are thought of as fearsome warriors. But many of them lived peaceful lives in small settlements.

Search & Find

- ☐ Boy sitting on dog
- ☐ Fires (3)
- ☐ Fishnet
- ☐ Goats (2)
- ☐ Horses (4)
- ☐ Man being hit with a fish
- ☐ Sleeping pig
- ☐ Sword seller

Long ship
Viking long ships were light and fast. These war ships were called "dragons" or "dragonships" by enemies.

Splitting wood
Logs were split apart to make flat boards.

Market
Food, cloth, and tools were just a few of the things sold at market.

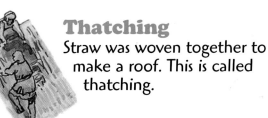

Thatching
Straw was woven together to make a roof. This is called thatching.

Knorr
Knorr (NOR) were smaller boats used to carry cargo.

Hanging hides
Animal skins (or hides) had to be hung up to dry. The skins were used for clothing or traded for other goods.

Find Out More on page 29

Medieval Times

Medieval (mid-EE-vul) times are also called the Middle Ages. Powerful men called lords lived in big castles. These castles were like small towns. Many people and animals lived and worked inside the walls of the castle.

Search & Find

- ☐ Cows (2)
- ☐ Crossbows (3)
- ☐ Crow
- ☐ Fireplaces (5)
- ☐ Flags (6)
- ☐ Pitchfork
- ☐ Smoking chimneys (6)

Jousting

In a joust, each knight would try to knock the other one off of his horse. The knights used a long pole called a lance.

Falconer

A falconer is a person who trains birds to hunt.

Blacksmith

Every town or village had a blacksmith. This one is making a horseshoe.

Cooks

Medieval cooks were almost always women. They served food to the people in the castle.

Knight

A knight served and protected a lord or a king. He rode on horseback while regular soldiers walked.

Guard

Guards often stood watch on the castle towers and at the gates.

Jester

The jester acted like a clown. He entertained the lord and his guests.

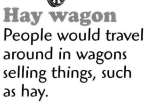

Hay wagon

People would travel around in wagons selling things, such as hay.

Find Out More on page 29

19

Aztecs

The Aztecs (AZ-teks) ruled a powerful empire in northern Mexico. They were fearless warriors. They were also farmers and weavers. The Aztecs enjoyed ball games, music, and dancing. They built great cities, pyramids, and temples.

Search & Find

- [ ] Cages (6)
- [ ] Drummers (3)
- [ ] Green feather fans (8)
- [ ] Juggler
- [ ] Parrots (7)
- [ ] Umbrellas (2)
- [ ] Voladors (flying men) (4)

Jaguar knight

A jaguar knight was a highly-honored Aztec Guard.

Macaw

A macaw is a large, colorful parrot found in Mexico, Central, and South America.

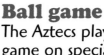

Ball game

The Aztecs played a ball game on special courts. They had to bounce the ball against the side walls and try to get it through a stone hoop.

Fruit seller

A farmer brought his crops to the market to sell.

Royal procession

Guards walked with the ruler. Helpers laid carpets for the ruler to walk on. His feet were not allowed to touch the ground.

Porter

A porter carries things for someone else.

Weavers

The Aztecs were skilled weavers. They wove cloth and baskets. Often, they wove symbols into their work to honor gods and nature.

Aztec drummer

Drumming and dancing were important to the Aztecs.

Find Out More on page 30

Spanish Galleon

A Spanish galleon (GA-lee-un) was a large sailing ship. It could carry many people and things across the ocean. The galleon was both a trading ship and a warship. Galleons were often called treasure ships. Pirates attacked them to steal the goods and treasure they carried back to Spain.

Search & Find

- ☐ Anchor
- ☐ Cat
- ☐ Cook
- ☐ Female pirate
- ☐ Flags (3)
- ☐ Mice (4)
- ☐ Monkey
- ☐ Shark head

Pirate
A pirate was a thief who attacked ships and stole things from them.

Cannon
Many cannons and other weapons were used to fight attackers.

Jolly Roger
The pirate flag, called the Jolly Roger, has a white skull and crossbones on a black background.

Ratlines

Sailors climbed up these rope ladders to get to the top of the tall masts.

Treasure

A galleon often carried gold, gems, coins, and other riches.

Lifeboat

A lifeboat is used to help people escape from a larger boat during an emergency.

Abandon ship

Sometimes the best way to escape a pirate attack was to jump off the ship.

Find Out More on page 30

Old West

Settlers began moving to the western United States about 150 years ago. They traveled by covered wagon and on horseback. It was a long and dangerous journey. But they were not the first people to live in the West. Native American tribes already lived there. Some tribes lived peacefully with the settlers. Others did not.

Sheriff

A sheriff was the top law officer in the area. He made sure people obeyed the law.

Chief

A chief is the leader of his tribe.

Papoose

A papoose is a Native American baby. Women from some tribes made a cradle that could be strapped to their back.

Horses

Horses were first brought to the Americas by the Spanish explorers.

Hitching post

This was like a parking spot for horses!

Prospector

A prospector searches for minerals. In the Old West, most prospectors were looking for gold and silver.

Stagecoach

A stagecoach took people to different places. It also carried mail. Trains would later take the place of stagecoaches.

Tepee

Many Native Americans lived in tents called tepees. They were made of animal skins stretched over poles.

Find Out More
on page 31

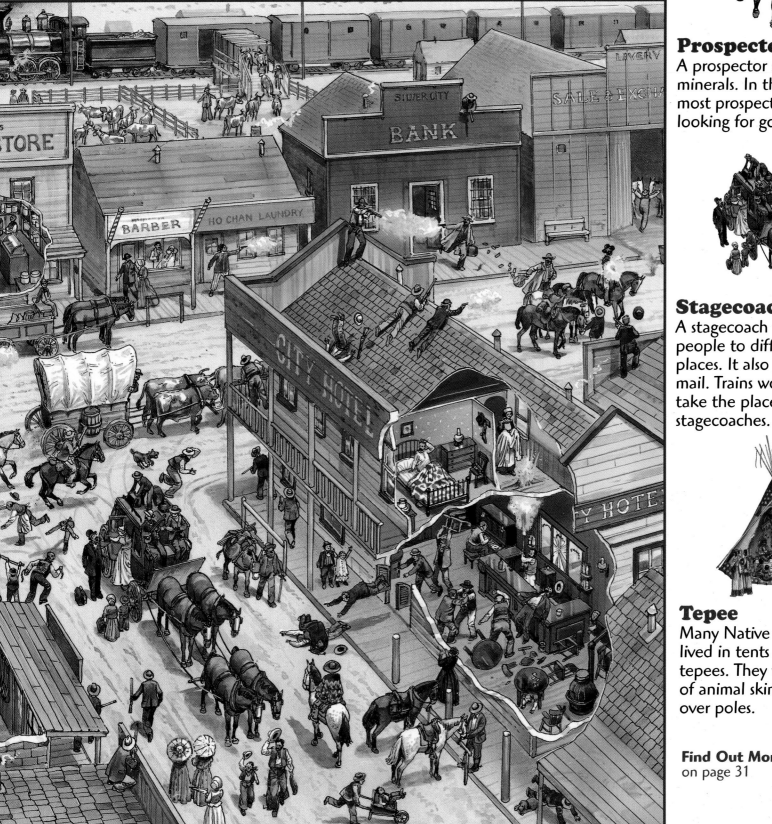

Find Out More

Early Humans

Early humans would often trade things, such as animal skins, with each other.

After they were cleaned, animal skins were stretched out to dry in the sun. They could then be softened with stones and made into clothes.

Sometimes men would walk far away to find animals to hunt.

Rocks were used to do many things. There were no metal objects.

Scientists still search for and study the remains of early humans.

A scientist who studies humans from long ago is called an archaeologist (AR-kee-AH-luh-jist).

The earliest known humans lived in Africa.

Learn more at:

www.pbs.org/wgbh/nova/stoneage/

http://leakeyfoundation.org/

http://amnh.org/exhibitions/atapuerca/

Ancient Egypt

Oxen were used to drag heavy blocks. Some blocks weighed more than 50,000 pounds!

A metal tool called a chisel was used to mark stone blocks.

When a heavy, wooden sled was dragged up the hot stones, it could catch fire. Water was poured on the ground to keep everything cool.

Ancient Egyptians believed that a person began a new life in another world after he or she died.

Pharaohs were carried in a sedan (suh-DAN) chair. Some often wore a colorful cloth on their head.

Learn more at:

www.ancientegypt.co.uk/menu.html

www.pbs.org/wgbh/nova/pyramid/explore/

Ancient Greece

Soldiers marched in lines, shoulder-to-shoulder.

Actors wore painted masks on stage. The masks told the audience what part the actor was playing.

Most plays had a chorus. A chorus was a group of people who sang and danced during the play.

The first Olympic Games were held in ancient Greece. There was only one event: a 210-meter foot race.

Learn more at:

www.enchantedlearning.com/olympics/

http://arwhead.com/Greeks/

Soldiers and athletes were very important in ancient Greece.

Ancient Rome

Important buildings were at the center of the city. The busy marketplace was always full of people.

The Colosseum is an ancient arena that was used for gladiator fights and other events. It is still one of Rome's most famous places to visit.

The ancient Romans were excellent builders. Many of their roads and buildings still stand today.

The month of July was named after Julius Caesar. He was a famous Roman leader.

The public baths were kept warm by an underground heating system.

Roman men took part in track and field events in a place called the Campus. Ball games and board games were also popular.

Learn more at:

www.bbc.co.uk/schools/romans/city.shtml

www.pbs.org/wgbh/nova/lostempires/roman/

www.roman-empire.net/children/

Great Wall of China

A scaffold is a raised platform. Workers stand or sit on a scaffold to work on things up high.

Any material that was close by was used to build the wall. Some parts of the wall were made of packed earth.

Workers carried stones from the quarry. They used baskets attached to a pole to carry the stones.

The Chinese invented gunpowder, which they used to fire cannons.

Guards were always present to protect the emperor.

The Great Wall of China runs for more than 2,000 miles. It is the longest wall in the world.

Learn more at:

www.enchantedlearning.com/subjects/greatwall/index.html

http://travelchinaguide.com/china_great_wall/

Vikings

The Vikings enjoyed having feasts. Some could last for over a week!

Most Vikings were very skillful sailors. They were the first Europeans to explore North America.

Deep wells were dug to find fresh water.

Vikings were also known as the Norse, or Norsemen. Old Norse is the language they spoke. Many English words came from Old Norse, such as *freckle*, *scare*, and *window*.

The Vikings traded for many different things. Here, cattle are loaded onto Viking ships.

A blacksmith heated iron in a fire to make it soft. Then he shaped it. He made tools, weapons, and horseshoes.

Learn more at:

www.bbc.co.uk/history/ancient/vikings/pbs.org/

www.pbs.org/wnet/warriorchallenge/vikings/

Medieval Times

The lord and lady of the castle held feasts. Musicians would often play for the guests.

The crossbow was an important weapon during the Middle Ages.

Most of the people who lived near the castle were called peasants. They farmed the land and gave crops to the lord. In return, the lord and his knights would protect the peasants.

Most castles were built on hills so that they would be easier to defend.

Spiral staircases made it easier for knights to fight attackers. Since they are open on one side, the knights had more room to use their sword.

A knight and his horse wore heavy armor while jousting. The armor protected them from getting hurt.

A knight's armor and shield usually had pictures or markings on them. These pictures and words told where the knight came from.

Learn more at:

www.learner.org/exhibits/middleages/

http://cybersleuth-kids.com/sleuth/History/Medieval/

Aztecs

Aztecs were famous for weaving feathers. Cloaks, shields and headdresses were made from colorful feathers. Birds were kept in a special building called an aviary (AY-vee-air-ee).

Temples were built at the top of the pyramids.

This man is dressed as Huitzilopochtli (HWEET-zee-loh-POKE-tlee), the god of war, sun, and nation. He is a blue god who holds a shield and a serpent that breathes fire.

Men dressed as birds, called voladors (VOH-lah-dorz), swung through the air during special ceremonies.

Early Aztecs called themselves the Mexica. This is where the name "Mexico" came from.

Ball games were very important to the Aztecs. The winners were treated like kings. The losers were often punished.

Learn more at:

www.pbs.org/conquistadors/cortes/cortes_a00.html

http://elbalero.gob.mx/kids/history/html/conquista/aztecas.html

http://mnsu.edu/emuseum/cultural/mesoamerica/aztec.html

Spanish Galleon

Galleons had either three or four levels, called decks. Food and drink were stored in barrels on the lower decks.

The crew slept in hammocks on lower decks. The captain slept in a bed in a room called the captain's quarters.

Pirates often fought with curved swords called cutlasses.

Several Spanish galleons were wrecked off the coast of Florida. This part of Florida is now called the Treasure Coast.

Extra sails and rigging were also kept on lower decks. Rigging is the chains, ropes, and other things needed to make the sails work.

Live animals were kept on board for use as food during the voyage.

Learn more at:

http://floridahistory.com/galleon.html

www.nhm.org/education/cahistory/galleon/

http://www.surfnetkids.com/pirates.htm

Old West

"The West" is the part of the United States that is west of the Mississippi and Missouri Rivers.

Some Native American tribes in the West were nomads. That means they moved often. Native Americans walked everywhere before horses were brought to the Americas.

Some people traveled west in wagon trains. These were groups of people traveling together on foot, on horseback, and in covered wagons.

The railroad was a faster way than wagons to carry people out west.

Trains had different cars to carry different things. Here, cattle are loaded into the cattle car.

The Old West is often called the Wild West. Sometimes outlaws robbed banks and railroads and then hid out in the woods. Even when there was a sheriff in town, it was a rough place to live.

The Pony Express was the first organized mail service across the West.

Learn more at:

www.pbs.org/weta/thewest/

http://americanwest.com/

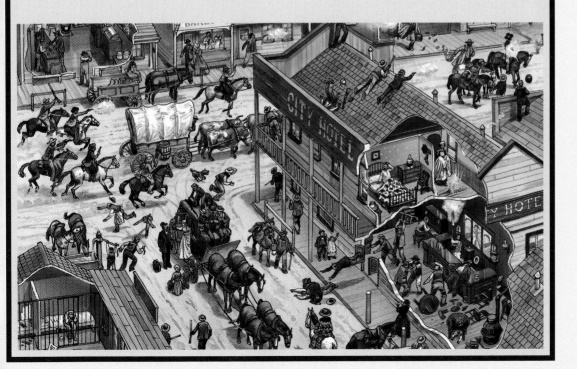

31